Workbook

For

Dare To Lead

Brave Work. Tough Conversations. Whole Hearts.

Genie Reads

Table of Contents

How To Use This Workbook 1

Introduction... 4

Part One: Rumbling with Vulnerability......... 11

Section One: The Moment and The Myths.... 11

Section Two: The Call To Courage 23

Section Three: The Armory.......................... 30

Section Four: Shame and Empathy.............. 45

Section Five: Curiosity and Grounded 57

Part Two: Living Into Our Values................. 65

Part Three: Braving Trust........................... 77

Part Four: Learning To Rise 84

Epilogue.. 88

May you lead courageously

How To Use This Workbook

Hello there!

It is with great pleasure to see that you have taken an interest in the book "Dare To Lead" by Brené Brown. This book by Brené is both an inspiration for leaders as well as a practical road map where one can hone their leadership skills. Taking responsibility, leading from the front and moving with courage are all features which are highlighted and expounded upon in the book. Through this multi-faceted approach, you will be able to develop and create your own courageous form of leadership based on sound fundamentals.

This workbook is meant to enhance and highlight the ideas and concepts mentioned, so that it makes it very much easier for you to take action and implement what you have learnt from the book into practical, daily usage. With the aid of this workbook, sharpening and bringing forth courageous leadership becomes much easier through the step by step guidance and systematic approaches highlighted within. Equipped with the knowledge and practical skillsets developed through the workbook's exercises, you can be sure that you will be able to master the principles of leading and bring forth impactful results for yourself and many others. In order to absorb quicker and with a lasting impact, it is vital that you answer all the questions presented in the workbook, and answer them sincerely. Only by digging deep and giving honest answers will you be able to flash light on what truly matters to you, and get the opportunities to effect lasting positive change in your daily life.

The workbook will also feature important summaries of each individual chapter, which will be integral in helping you answer the questions contained therein. As such, for the time constrained folk, you do not necessarily need to read the main book before answering the questions in this workbook. All the crucial points have been condensed and captured for your attention. For the folks whom have already read the book, the afore mentioned salient concepts will serve well as quick reminders and gentle nudges when you are doing the questions.

Whilst attempting the questions found in the workbook, please take your time to go through it carefully. This portion is an area where speedy reading can be set aside and replaced with thoughtful ruminations. The questions will encourage you to reflect and think, sometimes very deeply, before you jump in with any answers. It will be of great benefit to you if the answers supplied are colored with the honesty of thought and tinged with sincerity. After all, no one can be as interested in your welfare as your own self.

Done in this careful, constructive way, you will be able to harness the positive change created and see it reverberate throughout many aspects of your life. For some, the honest answers may create self criticism. Take heart, know that you are not alone, and that by just the mere act of acknowledgement of mistakes made in the past, that itself is a very important step forward.

You will want to come back to these questions again after your initial foray, say after a period of 4 to 8 weeks; there really is no set in stone time length, but it is highly recommended to have at least a space of 4 weeks between the first and second attempt at the questions. This second try is really to let you see the progress you have made, both in thoughts and actions, and also to think of different angles to the same questions with your new life experiences.

You can really repeat this process as many times as you find useful. The key is always honesty in the answers and an indefatigable spirit for self development and progress.

May you be well and be happy.

Introduction

Brené Brown defines a leader as someone who takes up the duty to find the potential in processes and people and has the sheer braveness to develop this potential. In writing this book, her goal is to teach you how to become one. *Dare to Lead* is a culmination of twenty years of data, including interviews with 150 global C-level leaders, program evaluation studies from her organization, Brave Leaders Inc., and data collected during a three-year instrument development study about daring leadership.

Brené used to be a research professor, but over the years, she also became the CEO and founder of her organization. The most humbling and difficult lesson she learned is that researching about leadership is much easier than the actual act of leading. By writing this book, her dream is not just to teach her readers to become great leaders; she also hopes to improve herself and create a world of brave leaders.

Dare to Lead is a practical playbook that transforms the lessons from Brené's previous books, *Daring Greatly* and *Rising Strong*, into actions. She was told to write what she needed to read. From her various interviews with leaders and as a leader herself, she knew this is what she needed to write.

To master the tools, skills, and language discussed in this book, you must dedicate time and effort to practice them and develop the necessary courage. The journey won't be easy, and you will face many obstacles and barriers. But Brené assures you that as long as you identify these issues and face them, they won't be enough to stop you from being brave.

We're living in a rapidly-changing and complex environment. And each day, we're faced with almost unmanageable situations and a heavy demand for innovation that we can't always cope with. With this, Brené and her team interviewed leaders, asking them what they would change, if needed, to succeed in this type of environment.

The leaders' replies were identical and can be summed up as needing more courageous cultures and braver leaders. But the leaders had different replies when asked to rationalize their reply to the first question. Most thought of courage as behavior but could not identify the needed skills to become brave leaders. But they could easily identify the different cultural and behavioral problems that stand in the way of pursuing a daring leadership:

1. Leaders do everything they can to avoid difficult conversations, such as giving and listening to criticism. Some leaders blame it on the absence of courage or appropriate conversational skills, while others believe it's an act of being polite and nice.

2. Some spend too much time dealing with troublesome behavior rather than addressing and acknowledging

feelings and fears that show themselves in times of change.

3. Some disregard trust due to the absence of empathy and connection.

4. Since people are scared of being judged, most team members are afraid to take calculated risks and share new ideas. Often, leaders only get an idea from groupthink.

5. Leaders are stuck on reassuring members after every failure, setback, and disappointment rather than spending money on strengthening internal processes.

6. Some leaders focus on shaming and blaming rather than teaching members to learn from mistakes and take accountability.

7. Some people choose not to engage in talks about inclusivity and diversity since they are afraid of doing something wrong in other people's eyes.

8. Teams are used to the process of hurrying into weak solutions. We must first identify the problem and its cause before solving the problem.

9. Values in organizations are based on aspiration rather than visible behaviors.

10. People are not growing and learning due to fear and perfectionism.

The list above presents not only common organizational issues but also internal issues that most leaders have. It portrays the struggle to lead through the uncomfortable. Besides, the organizational culture and work behaviors all stem from individual issues. Once Brené and her team identified these, they worked to determine the required skill set needed to build courage. They have developed a solution with continuous research, improving, testing, modifying, and retesting to end up with a proven method that works.

The Heart of Daring Leadership

1.   To be courageous, you must rumble with vulnerability and learn to deal with the situation, no matter how ugly it may seem.

Rumble is defined as a meeting, discussion, or conversation with a commitment to lean into vulnerability, stay curious, stay in the struggle of identifying problems and solving them, take a break and circle back if needed, and become fearless. This definition is the core of the book's chapters and embodies the four skill sets needed:

Rumbling with Vulnerability

Living into Our Values

Braving Trust

Learning to Rise

You must have the determination and ability to rumble with vulnerability to master the different skills. Without it, your efforts will be futile. This belief has been tested from family-owned microbusinesses to Fortune 50 companies and various branches of the U.S. military. It has been proven to bring positive results to both the leaders and the performance of team members.

2.   Self-love and self-awareness matter. Who we are is how we lead.

It's a common misconception to assume that the problem is who people are and not how they behave. It's the same when it comes to courage. Take fear as an example; it's one of the major emotions included in the problematic behaviors discussed earlier. However, its existence is not the issue. It's how we respond to it.

Feeling fear is not the barrier. Rather, it's the emotions, thoughts, and behaviors we act on when we are afraid. These are the actions we do to hide from vulnerability. It's important to learn the skills and tools that are discussed in the following chapters. One needed skill to succeed in this is practicing self-compassion and being patient with ourselves during our journey.

3.   Courage is contagious

This principle makes it imperative for daring leaders to connect to the people they lead. Daring leaders must care for their team. It's the only way they can breed courageous leaders.

The data gathered by Brené and her team made it clear that connection and care are crucial to creating productive and wholehearted relationships between leaders and team members. If you feel disconnected from your team, take no shame in trying to rebuild your connection with them. It shows how dedicated you are to fixing the issue, even if it's a "you" problem. However, if you are unwilling to fix it, perhaps you need to reconsider your role-you may not be fit to be a leader.

We live in a complex society, and it's the leaders' job to develop a space wherein our team members have the liberty to be true to themselves. Brené often tells teachers, some of our most important leaders, that they can't command students to take off their armor at home. Instead, teachers should be able to make the school a place for students to take off the weight they are carrying so they can breathe freely.

When the team members are troubled with discriminatory issues, such as sexism, racism, classism, or any other behaviors of fear-based leadership, they will be unable to thrive and contribute accordingly. Likewise, in an organization that tolerates armoring behaviors such as perfectionism, blaming, cynicism, shaming, and emotional stoicism, innovation will not develop as well.

A 50-year-old leader once told Brené that parents or coaches taught her behavioral traits. This leader shared that she can still picture how she learned each lesson during the toughest moments. She emphasized that everyone must learn this lesson, too.

As you move forward to the following chapters, remember that these skills in building courage are not new. The problem is that we could not develop these skills because it's too humane and messy to deal with. Simply put, we do not dare to talk about courage. But now is the right time. Put down your armor and get ready to enter the arena.

Part One: Rumbling with Vulnerability

Section One: The Moment and The Myths

Summary

It is not the critic who counts, not the man who points out how the strong man stumbles, or where the doer of deeds could have done them better. The credit belongs to the man who is actually in the arena, whose face is marred by dust and sweat and blood; who strives valiantly; who errs, who comes short again and again...who at best knows, in the end, the triumph of high achievement, and who at the worst, if he fails, at least fails while daring greatly - Theodore Roosevelt

Brené came across the above quote from Roosevelt at a time when she was facing career challenges. She found the quote meaningful and used it as an inscription in her book, Daring Greatly. The quote tells us that the man who never gives up deserves to be recognized. Brené learned three valuable lessons from this quote, which play an important role in the research of this book.

The first lesson taught Brené that every brave person accepts that they will eventually fail, yet they do not hesitate to give their best. The second lesson clarified that vulnerability is not synonymous with weakness; it is what we feel during times of risk, emotional exposure, and uncertainty while still showing up to face the music. The third lesson advises listening only to the truly brave people constantly putting themselves on the line—people speaking from experience and not just "preaching" or criticizing from the sidelines.

We all need a good dose of feedback, but they need to be from people worth listening to. Remember that if we shut ourselves off from listening to feedback, we stop learning and growing. But if we listen to any feedback, we risk getting too hurt by it that we tend to ignore the feeling until it festers within us. Sometimes, we tend to shield ourselves from this feedback until the shield becomes so impenetrable that we can no longer feel hurt or loved. When we fail to love, we lose vulnerability.

In her book, *Daring Greatly*, Brené suggests getting a one-inch square piece of paper to write down the names of people whose opinions matter. It is intended to be small, so you must choose wisely. List only the names of those who truly accept and love you despite your imperfections and vulnerability and whom you can trust to be brutally honest with you—your "square squad." That way, you maintain your vulnerability.

Myths About Vulnerability

There are six myths surrounding vulnerability:

Myth #1: "Vulnerability is weakness."

In 2014, Brené gave a talk to military soldiers and asked if they could give her a single example of courage that did not require being vulnerable. There was a long silence before someone answered that in his three tours, he never witnessed or experienced anything courageous that did not require him to be vulnerable.

Myth #2: "I don't do vulnerability."

Every day, we experience different risky and uncertain situations that make us vulnerable. It's either we own these vulnerabilities or let them own us. Only by embracing our vulnerability can we fully understand our emotions and how they influence our thoughts and behavior to remain aligned with our values. When we pretend we are not vulnerable, we allow fear to rule our life, and how we express that fear can never be good for us. Our "square squad" can jolt us into reality, so we should carefully select them.

For example, you've worked hard and contributed much to achieving your company's goals. You expect to be recognized as this month's Top Performer. To your dismay, it was awarded to somebody relatively new. You refused to admit to anybody, including yourself, that the situation hurt you. The result: you became difficult to work with and lost the fire to be at the top of your game.

Myth #3: "I can go it alone."

We all need someone to be with us or stand by us. Each of us experiences vulnerability which is why we could easily find comfort in opening up to people who understand and will not judge us. Based on neuroscientific studies, human beings are social creatures meant to connect—our neural systems are shaped for interdependence and togetherness instead of independence and aloneness. Any attempt to go against this biological makeup will most likely lead to loneliness and suffering.

Myth #4: "You can engineer the uncertainty and discomfort out of vulnerability."

Several tech companies have hinted that systems and structures can take vulnerability out of the success equation. A rocket scientist once told Brené that vulnerability has no place in his job. When Brené pressed him to name the most challenging part of his job, he realized that he had the most sophisticated systems but struggled with leading and managing his team.

Myth #5: "Trust comes before vulnerability."

Trust and vulnerability go hand in hand. Trust is needed to be vulnerable, while we also need to show vulnerability to be able to trust. Ellen, Brené's daughter, came home one day after a bad day in school. The girl told her mother that she had told only her friends about what happened but was disappointed to learn that everyone in her class knew about it by the end of the day.

In Ellen's class, there is a jar filled with marbles. For each good decision the class collectively makes, they are allowed to put in marbles; but for every bad collective decision, the teacher takes out some of the marbles. When Ellen was shamed, the teacher removed plenty of marbles from the jar because many of Ellen's classmates laughed at her. And that worsened an already bad day for Ellen.

Brené wanted to protect her daughter but instead advised Ellen to share her secrets with only those friends she could fully trust.

Moreover, trust is earned by accumulating small gestures and deeds of goodness, not with a single grand act.

Myth #6: "Vulnerability is disclosure."

Vulnerability does not mean an open, random sharing of emotions and personal experiences. It is about creating a safe environment for people where a leader asks their team members what will make them feel safe and open in a conversation. This approach is a good, practical way to build the trust of team members and make conversations relevant. It also means setting boundaries to know what is acceptable and what is not. Without setting boundaries, vulnerability becomes desperation, manipulation, fear, or anxiety.

It is not about seeking sympathy by voicing out your fears and showing your helplessness; it is about engaging in conversations to seek advice on moving forward despite the fear. For example, leaders going through extreme anxiety because of uncertainties brought about by difficult organizational changes should not reveal to their team members that they do not know how to move forward because the team members might lose their trust in the team leader. Instead, they should seek out people who can guide them to overcome the challenges.

Experiencing different emotions, no matter how strong we are, makes us vulnerable. And since we are emotional creatures, it is natural to be vulnerable. Take away vulnerability, and we lose our creativity because we shut off uncertainties that drive us to innovate.

Leaders need to be resilient and ethical in their choices. They should be able to give and receive feedback effectively and solve problems—no matter how complex they might be. And all these begin with being vulnerable.

Lessons

1. Vulnerability does not equate to weakness. It's what we feel when we embrace risk and uncertainty.

2. Genuinely loving someone is the most vulnerable act.

3. Learning how to filter the feedback or opinions we hear every day is important. We must learn to listen to those who truly matter.

4. A truly brave person already knows he is destined to fail, yet that will not stop him from trying.

5. No one is immune from vulnerability. It's the reason why we are capable of comforting one another since we can all relate to it.

6. Setting up clear boundaries is important in relationships, including work. These boundaries define what is acceptable and what is not and explain why.

Issues Surrounding the Subject Matter

1. Why do you think people fear being vulnerable?

2. Can you think of a time when you have shown vulnerability? What was the situation? What made you feel vulnerable, and how did you manage the situation? How did it end up?

3. Was there ever a time when you have foregone setting boundaries? If yes, why did you not set boundaries? What was the outcome?

4. Have you experienced feeling vulnerable but chose to mask it with an I-am-not-bothered attitude? Why did you choose to hide it? How did it affect you?

5. Have you experienced trusting someone and sharing with them a secret, only to realize that they betrayed you? What problems did you face as a result of that? How did you deal with them?

Goals

1. How will you unlearn the myths of vulnerability?

2. What will you do to set boundaries without offending anyone?

3. How can you shield yourself from hurt while opening yourself up to other people's feedback?

Action Steps

1. Observe how you and other people react in tough situations.

   a. Describe the situation. What made it a tough situation?

   b. How did the people involved in the situation behave towards each other before, during, and after? What do you think made you or the people involved react that way?

c. What do you think could have been handled better?

d. If the situation were to happen again, what should you or the people involved do to transform the situation into something positive?

2. Identify your square squad.

a. Use a 1-inch square sheet of paper to limit the names on your list.

b. List down the names of people you can trust and rely on to give honest feedback.

c. Review this list now and then so you can update it as needed.

3. Communicate to people what is okay with you and what is not.

a. It would help to explain why some things are not okay with you.

b. During difficult situations, ask other people involved what they can comfortably and openly share and what is off-limits. That way, you show respect for their vulnerability.

4. Apply a modified version of the marble jar metaphor. Keep a record of the pluses and minuses done by people you think of as friends.

   a. Put a star, a heart, or any symbol next to the name of a friend each time they make you feel good about yourself, e.g., by giving you a kind word.

   b. However, remove one of those symbols each time someone does something to hurt you, e.g., break your trust.

Checklist

1. Have a 1- inch square paper where you can list the names of your square squad.

2. Use a journal for your marble jar metaphor and another for your observations. It doesn't matter if you use a digital or a traditional journal.

3. Decide how frequently you would like to review the names on your square squad list.

4. Schedule tough conversations with the people you are with to set boundaries. Prepare yourself emotionally and mentally for each conversation.

Section Two: The Call To Courage

Summary

Despite studying leadership, the author, Brené, also has her struggles in leading. In this section, she opens up about the time her team confronted her about how she sets unreasonable deadlines that her team can never meet.

Brené admitted that it was not the first time she had heard of this. She recalled a situation when her husband also pointed out that she is not good at estimating time. It was painful to hear it again from her team, but she was also thankful that they opened it to her directly.

She wanted, more than anything, to end the conversation and get it over with. But instead, she promised to give them a solution the next day. Brené highlighted the importance of having enough thinking time before coming to a resolution. Instead of pushing the issue out of the way, it is wiser to have a much-needed break before the people involved get together for a tough conversation.

That night, she researched what she could do to change her habit of setting tight deadlines but realized that her problem was not specifically her lack of sense of time or project management. It was because she was living in fear and anxiety. She expressed how important it is to go back to the root cause of the issue to resolve the problem rather than make empty promises by giving temporary solutions that provide short-term relief.

Joseph Campbell once said, "The cave you fear to enter holds the treasure you seek." Brené used this quote as an analogy to her situation. The first question asks, "What is the treasure I seek?" For Brené, it was to reduce her anxiety, fear, and feeling of scarcity. She wanted to work with her team to reach goals that excite and motivate everyone.

The next question is, "What is the cave I fear to enter?" Brené bravely owned her fault for not practicing things real leaders ought to do. She was also scared to make wrong decisions and did not want to admit it to her team.

The next day came, and it was time for their "circle back" meeting. Brené permitted herself to be honest with them and narrated everything she had realized the night before. Then, as a team, they established some key learnings that would allow them to resolve the issue.

First, they established a new meeting minutes process wherein a person is assigned to take minutes. But whenever the team agrees on something, anyone can speak up and propose to include the agreement in the minutes. They allocated five minutes towards the end of the meeting to review the minutes to ensure they covered every significant discussion point. The minute-taker sends everyone a copy of the minutes immediately after the meeting.

Then, Brené's team came up with the "turn and learn" approach to establishing deadlines and setting priorities. With this approach, meeting attendees write on a sticky note certain projects by priorities and how long they think they can accomplish each project. When everyone has finished writing, they simultaneously show the team what they have written. That way, it fights off the halo effect, in which the team members determine their estimates based on what the most influential team member wrote. The approach also avoids the bandwagon effect or following the majority even if you think otherwise.

The last one is known as "gritty faith and gritty facts." This approach is their new rule wherein everyone is responsible for dreaming and doing a reality check by citing facts. But admittedly, when the going gets tough, it's still possible for everyone to slip into old habits and patterns., So, it's important to remind each other occasionally.

Brené shared another story of a leader calling for courage. It's about Colonel DeDe Halfhill's experience as she led the Air Force Global Strike Command. She pointed out that every leader is familiar with vulnerability, but their language differs. Words are very important in connecting with those who we lead.

In Colonel Halfhill's case, she realized that to connect with the airmen, she had to be vulnerable with them without using the word. Many airmen had come forward to admit that the immense feeling of loneliness lies underneath the exhaustion they were complaining about. She began a difficult conversation, which ended with a discussion on how they could connect and build a community that supports each other.

Colonel Hafhill also realized the importance of the message we convey as leaders, be they expressed in words or actions. In her case, she was torn between speaking about loneliness to her team because she's not trained for it, and it might cause more damage. On the other hand, sending them to a professional therapist might make her team members think they are being sent away and feel more isolated.

With this incident, she also researched their leadership manuals and found that the manual used decades ago was much more honest when discussing words such as connection, feelings, love, and the like. But as the years progressed, the modern manuals only discussed tactics and strategies. The colonel pointed out that leaders need to take it upon themselves to teach it to their people.

Both stories have shown leaders being vulnerable enough to be courageous in different circumstances. In doing so, these leaders must take time to tackle feelings and fears. These emotions are crucial in conducting daily tasks, which ultimately help in making any organization work smoothly.

Lessons

1. Confrontation with clarity is being kind.

2. Allow yourself and your team enough thinking time before resolving an issue. It will help you come up with a sound decision.

3. When caught in a problem, figure out the source and deal with that rather than headbutting the problem.

4. It's a leader's job to become comfortable with uncomfortable situations and talk about feelings and fears. Negative emotions cause strained relationships and poor productivity.

5. Words are very important when calling to courage; leaders must ensure that their team connects and relates to the vocabulary used.

Issues Surrounding the Subject Matter

1. Can you remember a certain event in your organization that was uncomfortable but also necessary? What made it uncomfortable? How did you handle it? Could you have handled it better than you did? How?

2. What treasure are you hunting for in your life right now? Why do you seek it? What is the cave you refuse to answer? Why? What will make you enter that cave?

3. Think of a difficult situation you experienced or witnessed where the people involved pushed to resolve the issue immediately. What was the situation about? Did they succeed at resolving it? Why or why not? What could they have done better?

4. Recall the loneliest time of your life. How did your loneliness affect you and your actions? How did you deal with your loneliness?

Goals

1. How will you handle a difficult situation with your team members?

2. What should you do to help your team members manage their vulnerability?

3. Learn how to portray vulnerability without using the word.

Action Steps

1. Set up new rules that would help resolve your issues based on what you have discussed with your team.

2. Depending on how frequently your team needs it, conduct casual meetings without talking about work.

3. Be open with your team and understand that you must be clear with their expectations.

Checklist

1. Document your new rules on a nice paper sheet and post them so everyone can see and be reminded of them.

2. Agree on a fixed time and date for your regular meetings and have everyone put it on their calendar. For extra measure, send a reminder to everyone a day before the meeting.

3. Let everyone take turns writing the minutes of the meeting, and be sure to review them before ending the meeting.

Section Three: The Armory

Summary

Due to messed-up notions of what makes a successful business, employers push their employees to deliver perfection at all times. They reward those who are stoic and relentless in their drive to achieve goals no matter how difficult and think less of employees who express emotions such as frustration and anxiety. As a result, we have unconsciously built organizations that push back normal emotions to focus on being right and all-knowing.

This practice restricts the heart and, in turn, kills courage. But since we are naturally egotistical beings, we do not always mind suppressing our emotions as long as our ego is fed. It sure feels great to be accepted, approved of, and praised constantly. And because of that feeling of greatness, the ego will do everything to avoid vulnerability.

This greatness is why we are so hellbent on protecting our egos by putting armors around us instead of setting our hearts free. When the ego is threatened, it will lead to shame. It's a feeling that we experience that makes us doubt ourselves.

Below are sixteen examples of how armored leadership responded with a daring leadership resolution:

1. Contrary to common belief, perfectionism is not synonymous with excellence, healthy achievement, growth, or success. Rather, it's driven by shame. Team members should be able to discuss signs of perfectionism and differentiate them from their actual goals—successful conversations about this lead to better performance.

   A perfectionist team member would do anything to retain their image of perfection. It could mean going to extreme lengths to reach unattainable goals. It's because of their fear of failure and shame. A daring leader would eliminate this by opening up conversations about this during rumbles. It's easy to spot perfectionism when familiar with its red flags and warning signs.

2. Based on statistics, almost 90 percent of us imagine the worst after experiencing something joyful. Some leaders refuse to celebrate achievements at work to avoid employees becoming too excited because they fear it will welcome bad events. On the contrary, it's better to practice gratitude. Celebrating through recognition programs is motivational and encourages them to show gratitude.

This practice is most common, especially among parents. Parents would look at their children with admiration and reflect on their love. And in the next second, they are picturing what they would do if something bad happened to their child. Joy is a sign of vulnerability, so we are afraid of staying in this emotion for too long. The best way to conquer this feeling is to practice gratitude. Go back to your children or anyone you love and be thankful for their presence in your life.

3. Numbing comes in different forms. It could be through alcohol, drugs, smoking, shopping, etc. Regardless, every one of us has been through it at some point. It's almost normal for humans to turn to numbing when a situation requires us to be vulnerable. To combat this, we should remember that the act is not the difference between numbing and real comfort. It's the reason why we do it.

Numbing sets in when the stress increases. Sometimes, it is unintentional. For example, when on top of your full-time job, you are working multiple side jobs, maintaining a household, and trying to start a business. The load gets so much that you no longer know what to prioritize. So instead, you would go drinking every night rather than allowing yourself to become vulnerable by facing the problem and solving it. All because it's easier than confronting your problem.

4. Most of us grew up believing in the concept of binaries: you are either the crusher or the crushed. This mindset causes people to believe that one must be invincible to succeed at all times; however, this is not true. The best way to counter this is by bringing together all of our qualities and making them work toward our goals.

   Brené interviewed people who lead from a Viking or Victim perspective. These people often describe success as survival or winning. In some cases, it's true. But when you remove the threat, survival is not living. A daring leader should operate with a strong back, soft front, and a wild heart. It draws away the desire to "crush" others just to succeed.

5. Then, there are knowers and learners. Knowers carry heavy baggage, and sometimes, it's not even their fault. Some people are only valued as knowers and nothing else. Being a knower causes the pressure to be right all the time. But to be a leader, we should also know how to ask the right questions, which is sometimes a struggle for knowers. Transitioning from knower to learner is a

struggle but can be worked out when focusing on becoming curious.

It may sound easy, but it can be a real struggle for knowers. Most of them need to unlearn to be able to learn. There are three steps to transforming into someone who is always learning. The first is to name the issue. It will be a difficult issue, but clarity is kindness. Second, you must prioritize learning curiosity skills. And lastly, reward (or at least acknowledge) great questions as daring leadership behavior.

6. Sarcasm and cynicism cover up internal emotions and inflict anger, hurt, and resentment. With both present at work, a toxic environment is formed. Instead of this toxicity, be a leader who promotes kindness, clarity, and honesty. Most importantly, be a leader who cultivates hope.

Some consider sarcasm quirky and sometimes linked to intelligence or wit. It might be true, but it's rarely helpful in the work environment. It's a cheap way to respond because it's easy to take shots at others which is why it's sometimes rewarded. It's wrong. Always choose clarity and kindness over this type of behavior.

7. Criticism can present itself through nostalgia and the invisible army. Nostalgia can be seen when a person refuses to change because of what they are used to; meanwhile, an invisible army is when a certain person always uses "we" in disagreeing when it's just them. Supporting every criticism with a more suitable contribution is important in bold leadership.

    Brené hated this type of behavior. She narrated that when a new idea is introduced, sometimes, someone reacts by saying, "We've never done it that way" or "We don't want to change course." Her co-leaders often need to stop her from saying, "Who's we?" Trying to pretend that lots of people represent you is cheap behavior. Rather, learn to contribute. In this case, if you are not a fan of the idea, state the reason why and suggest how you would do it differently. That way, it shows that you took a risk and made a contribution.

8. Power isn't essentially good or bad, depending on how it's used. The recurring problem is those who use power over others, especially minorities. There are three other ways to implement power positively: to use power with others as a team, make significant changes, and amplify each individual's power within.

Instead of *power over*, try to practice *power with, power to*, and *power within*. *Power with* refers to finding strength in a group. With mutual support, you are stronger than being alone. *Power to* refers to giving everyone in your team the opportunity to utilize their potential. Everyone has a certain skill set that is unique to them, and they may use it to help the team. *Power within* is the ability to acknowledge differences and learn how to respect others. It's about learning ways to achieve the desired greater good.

9. When individuals do not recognize their strength in the company, they tend to do everything to prove their worth. This reaction causes them to go around and not contribute something worthwhile. Daring leaders should be able to identify where their team is strong. Recognizing strengths would allow the individual to be a great contributor.

For instance, a technical person may have the talent and the grit to excel. But if he is in an environment that only rewards sales contributions, they might be tempted to do everything and anything to be recognized—even unethical ways just to be rewarded. As a leader, you should be able to assess your people's strengths. In this case, if you transfer this person to the IT department, they could easily contribute to the improvement and overall well-being of the organization.

10. Armored leaders focus on giving tasks, to-do lists, and checklists to ensure that their team does everything according to how they want it done. Some even go as far as monitoring the members' compliance every step. In return, their team would only do these things for compliance and for fear of getting caught. This attitude is not productive. On the other hand, daring leaders ensure that their team understands the purpose and goal of the task so that the team members can focus on achieving its goal, not on the specifics of how it's done.

For example, a telco company conducts regular sales calls with a minimum engagement of fifteen per member daily. The manager just states it like that and penalizes anyone who will not be able to reach the minimum. In return, the members would go through the calls without sincerity because they do not understand what it is for and are afraid to be called out. They would have treated it differently if the manager had explained that the reason was to generate more inorganic sales and that the number of engagements was based on their previous month's statistics.

11. Leveraging fear is common with leaders, especially in highly stressful times. They tend to point to a certain enemy and make their team work due to fear of this person. A good leader would acknowledge the fear and guide their team along the way. They show support to allow the team to perform well still.

    It would be easy to paint a picture of a manager triggering the changes and pretending or acting like a victim. If you are doing this to pressure your team to work aggressively because of their fear, you are weaponizing their emotions for your advantage. You can always admit fear without instilling it in them. Let them feel that you are with them throughout the difficult experience.

12. We all know it is not healthy to be sleep-deprived, yet we continue to tire ourselves to the point of no rest. But according to a psychiatrist, Dr. Stuart Brené, play and rest is needed to live a meaningful life. Most importantly, it allows us to renew ourselves after working tirelessly.

    An example of this is rewarding people who are constantly working overtime just to finish their tasks for the day. It's not supposed to be rewarded because employees are all given eight hours daily to finish their daily tasks. If they are not done with it within the said hours, then something is wrong with their productivity or efficiency, or it could be they are simply overloaded with too much work. Do not romanticize this type of work behavior. Rather, promote rest, play, and recovery. If you do this, people return to work, re-energized and happy.

13. Each one of us wants to belong and be accepted. Some even change themselves to fit in. Leaders should be able to promote a culture of diversity that allows every individual to be themselves without being judged and be completely part of the group.

Newly hired employees are usually the ones who experience trying hard to fit in with the team. The tenured members would already have a group, and if they do not like the newbie vibe, they will go out of their way to make themselves feel superior. Leaders should not tolerate this kind of behavior. Newbies should feel the excitement, and they should be celebrated for becoming the newest member of the team.

14. In the early years of a career, it's normal for an individual to collect achievements, awards, and medals. It helps them realize their worth in a company. However, it should no longer be the goal when promoted to leadership roles. The focus should be on developing the different members of the team and rewarding them.

    Tenured leaders should know when their time is up already, not in retirement but in the journey of receiving rewards. You should not jeopardize your team's performance for the sake of medals. Train your members the way the leader before you trained you. It's important to pass on the legacy.

15. In times of vulnerability, armored leaders tend to avoid or zigzag away from it, only prolonging the agony of having the issue up in the air. Instead, a daring leader would face problems head-on rather than do any delaying tactics. It's difficult, but it's the truth, and at the end of the day, the problem still needs to be resolved.

    For example, when you have made a mistake at work and must inform your supervisor about it. You employ different delaying tactics to justify why you can't inform your supervisor immediately. You may convince yourself that you have a million other things that you must finish first. Then by the end of the day, you figure it's too late to make the call and decide to do it the next day. The next day comes, and you still find another excuse not to do it. You let the days go by until it's too late for you to act on it.

16. When an individual leads from hurt, they tend to over-achieve to prove their worth and undo the pain they have experienced in the past. The catch is that no matter how hard we work, the pain will not be erased. Rather, we should face our fears and not let them interfere with our leadership role. We need to focus on the goal.

   Some young students who may have been mistreated by their teachers growing up may pursue a career in teaching when they are of age. However, their bad experience with their teacher may have been ingrained in them, and they treat their students the way their former teachers treated them. This situation is not healthy, and it would not heal any past wounds. The pain would keep on passing on. It's your choice to do things right and make a difference.

It's easy to disengage and hide behind the armor when faced with risky or challenging situations. When it becomes uncomfortable, it's a no-brainer to avoid the situation. However, this is not productive and will not help us improve as leaders or our team to be great contributors.

It will always start with daring leadership. Leaders should be able to face these uncomfortable or tough situations and be honest with their team. It's time to put down the armor and be vulnerable enough to be a brave and daring leader.

Lessons

1. Being wholehearted means being courageous.

2. The ego is one of the main reasons why we hide our emotions

3. There's always a daring way of leading as long as we face problems and difficult situations head-on.

4. Perfectionism is not a requirement for excellence; it's a disturbing attitude that could negatively affect work behavior.

5. Gratitude goes a long way for employees. It motivates them to know they are appreciated.

6. Situations are not always black and white. You do not have to crush someone else to succeed.

7. Leaders should lead as learners, not knowers.

Issues Surrounding the Subject Matter

1. Why do you think it's easier for leaders to hide behind the metaphorical armor?

2. Was there a time when you felt shame? How did it manifest in your work and your relationships? How did you navigate through it?

3. Which among the different armored leadership behaviors have you noticed in your organization? How has it affected your team? Your achievement of goals? What could have been done differently?

Goals

1. How would you start facing problems or issues? How do you intend to deal with them?

2. How can you avoid armored leadership?

3. What should you do to conquer your fears?

Action Steps

1. Always be grateful. Start a gratitude journal to list all things you should be thankful for. It could be a physical or digital journal; make sure you do it daily.

2. Prepare a monthly or quarterly recognition program for your staff. Recognize and reward your team for something they earned. Do not recognize people just for the sake of doing it. Remember that it should also be focused on gratitude.

3. Conduct regular huddles to cultivate a culture of belonging and ask individuals how they are. Diminish cliques that make your staff feel like they do not belong.

Checklist

1. Set aside five to ten minutes daily to write something in your gratitude journal. Your entries need not be about great things. You can be thankful even for little things.

2. Be specific with what your team members are being recognized for. Make them feel you are paying attention to each of them.

3. Huddles are usually about the priorities of the day or pressing issues that need to be addressed. Make your regular huddles about the team members more than anything else.

Section Four: Shame and Empathy

Summary

Shame is a powerful emotion and is one of the strongest factors that make us resist vulnerability. To illustrate, Brené shared a personal experience that happened in 2017. Her Rising Strong book tour ended in July 2017, and her other book Braving the Wilderness, was set to release on September 12 of the same year.

Brené had her mind set on renewing herself before the tour started to regain her energy and enjoy the planned activities and big events. After three weeks of preparation, she had a schedule to record the audiobook Braving the Wildnerness. During the recording, her producer asked Brené to remove her earrings since it was making a noise. When Brené removed it, she unexpectedly fell and was later diagnosed with a severe concussion.

Her team worked to cancel dates and adjust her schedule. Brené was pissed and refused to back down. One of the primary causes of shame is unwanted identities. For Brené, it was about being unreliable, sick, and undependable. Five days after the accident, she could not function well yet pushed harder to work even when she could not focus on anything. Beyond the shame of being sick, she was also ashamed of losing her ability to think straight.

Eventually, Brené and her husband, Steve, booked an appointment to see the Houston Rockets neuropsychologist specializing in concussion management. Brené was told that the fear she was feeling was normal. She was also given strategies to live with it. Then, Hurricane Harvey hit their neighborhood the next day.

It was heartbreaking, but in these times, her community leaned on each other and helped one another. Their healing journey was driven by kindness and empathy, which kept shame away. The book tour was launched on time. Brené described the memory as both hard and beautiful.

Take a look at these examples of shameful experiences based on Brené's interviews:

- Got fired from a job during a challenging time
- Hid substance addiction from other people
- Concealed a fault at work and got caught by the manager
- Failed business venture after convincing friends to invest in it
- Experienced sexual harassment but got too afraid to speak out

We must understand that shame is felt by each of us differently. It's also common for us to be scared of talking about it. Ironically, the more we avoid it, the more control it has over us. The experiences might be different per individual, but the emotion is still the same. Retreating or putting on armor is easier than tackling it.

Vocabulary is another factor that makes shame difficult to talk about. Shame is often confused with the words guilt, humiliation, and embarrassment when in reality, they all mean something else. Shame is not a moral compass; it causes an individual to become hurtful or destructive, which is different from the other words mentioned. It's best to start clearing these misconceptions caused by our choice of words to comprehend shame.

Guilt is felt when we have done something wrong and causes us to correct our wrongdoings; it promotes change. Humiliation is less destructive than shame, and it's when we know that it's not a "me" problem and we still work to solve the issue at hand. Meanwhile, embarrassment is the least serious among these emotions; it's normally just a fleeting feeling, and we can be over it in a few minutes.

Shame in organizations manifests in various ways such as discrimination, favoritism, gossiping, cover-ups, etc. It could be because it stems deep from the organization's culture if it's easy to detect. It's also not just in large companies but even schools and faith communities.

A common example where shame could present itself in an organization is in the act of firing someone. It's important to let go of people while allowing them to keep their dignity. It's not about avoiding a difficult conversation but rather realizing that you are dealing with human beings with feelings. How you let them off will bear a significant effect on them. Always think of the person, even when you need to do what you must for your company.

Shame resilience is something we can learn. The ability to move from shame to empathy is the real antidote. Empathy is just an empty word unless transformed into a skill and put into practice. Being empathetic does not mean minimizing the other person's pain. Instead, you need to acknowledge and connect the pain to a person's emotion.

Brené shared that during one of her most memorable vulnerable moments, her COO, Suzanne, empathized with her. It helped her greatly since Suzanne did not try to comfort or assure her that it would be okay because the truth was that it would not be. Brené was heartbroken about her situation, but she never felt alone throughout it.

Another important thing to understand is that empathy is not about fixing problems; it's about being there through it all without trying to push the emotions away. However, boundaries also play an important part. You must not make their problems yours because you would both be stuck in the same place.

Empathy requires five skills.

First is the skill to acknowledge other people's perspectives. People see the same picture differently because of differences in abilities, ages, beliefs, ethnicities, and races. It's not about seeing things from a different perspective but more about accepting and acknowledging that everyone has a unique perspective of everything. Their truth is no less true than your truth.

Second is the skill of withholding judgment. Judging has become a vicious shame cycle: because we are hurt by how others have judged us, we look for reasons to judge others so that they, too, will feel the shame we've been through.

The **third** and **fourth** skills circle emotional literacy, and they go hand in hand. One is the skill of understanding how other people feel in a certain situation, and the other is the skill of communicating how you understood the other person's feelings. Both skills allow us to be aware of our emotions and develop fluency in the language of emotions.

The **fifth** skill is mindfulness, or, as Brené put it, paying attention. It's about carefully observing a person's body language while opening up about their feelings. This skill is crucial because empathetic misses might arise from exaggerating or minimizing emotions. There's no ready empathetic response to a situation because each individual is unique.

An empathetic miss, clinically known as an empathetic failure, is that feeling you get when you're emotionally exposed yet not correctly understood. It's important to open up to the right person at the right time and be the right person to come to.

There are six common ways in which we see empathetic misses.

Empathy vs. Sympathy

Sympathy is when someone feels for you, while empathy is when someone feels with you. The former is a miss since it will make you feel alone, while the latter makes you feel understood and connected, allowing you to forge ahead.

Gasp and Awe

Sometimes, we share our shame with another person. After hearing our story, they gasp and tell you how bad your situation is and are visibly horrified by it. Instead of getting assurance from them, you end up comforting them.

The Mighty Fall

When someone views you as invincible, and you open up to them about your unfortunate experience, some would show disappointment in you. This reaction is another miss. Instead of empathizing with you, they show that you didn't meet their expectations, making you feel worse.

The Block and Tackle

It's also an empathetic miss when someone would respond by scolding you or showing that they are pissed. By doing so, they refuse to be with you and bring you out from your discomfort, so they would rather judge you.

The Boots and Shovel

Some think it's okay to lift you by saying that "you're great, you're awesome," in reaction to a shameful experience you confided. It's another miss because you would feel like they are lying to you by faking compliments.

"If You Think That's Bad..."

Some would respond by telling their worse-than-yours experience. This response is not helpful because you would feel guilty for feeling bad in the first place. Instead of focusing on your emotions, attention shifts to them.

In this journey of learning and practicing empathy, we must learn to be compassionate and kind, especially to ourselves. Brené shared a story where she said something bad during an interview, and in response, she beat herself up for it and made herself extremely bad. In reality, if it were her family or friends opening up to her about making the same mistake, she would be understanding and overall empathetic.

We must also familiarize ourselves with the elements of shame resilience. Remember that if we choose the right person to open up to, someone who is empathetic and understanding, shame will not survive. The first element is about recognizing shame. Most of us circle back to our shame shields, such as hiding, withdrawing, or keeping to ourselves. Knowing your shame shields allows you to notice it early and think it through before doing something bad.

Another element talks about seeing the bigger picture. Realize that you are not the only one experiencing the same experience, which minimizes the chance of staying ashamed. The third element is learning to open up; no one can help you when you are not saying anything. It leads to self-blame, disconnection, and fear. Lastly, do not be afraid to speak about shame - it thrives in silence. Learning to speak about it freely and fight it with empathy is the main goal of this section.

Lessons

1. Shame is one of the most common emotions that everyone feels. It is the painful experience or feeling that you are flawed and unworthy of everything good.

2. Shame, humiliation, embarrassment, and guilt are all different emotions. Humiliation is knowing that despite what happened, you know you are not at fault. Guilt is felt when we have done something against our values. Embarrassment is just a fleeting, normally funny emotion. It's not as deep as shame is.

3. Praising someone sharing their shame is not helpful at all; neither is sympathizing with them.

4. Empathy is the antidote to shame.

5. Shame can present itself through teasing, blaming, harassment, discrimination, etc.

6. Leaders who lead with empathy can erase shame in the organization.

Issues Surrounding the Subject Matter

1. What makes empathizing with another person difficult?

2. Why do you think it is easy to think of empathy misses as helpful?

3. Which of the empathy misses have you committed or been subjected to? How did it make you feel? How has it affected your relationship with the people involved?

4. In Brené Brown's story, she talked about denying help and rest when she needed it. Do you have a similar story? How did it go? When you look back at that memory, what would you change about it?

Goals

1. How can you develop empathy?

2. How can you avoid committing empathy misses?

3. How can you talk about shame comfortably?

Action Steps

1. Jot down each situation where you practiced one or more empathy skills. Indicate how you felt about doing it and how the other person reacted to you.

2. If you are the one sharing your shame, think of how the other person made you feel and how you would have handled it if you were in their place.

3. Encourage your team to talk about shame and educate them on how to empathize by sharing your experiences. Tell them how the people you shared your situation with reacted and how it made you feel. Hearing about your story will help them understand shame and empathy more than just explaining concepts and principles.

Checklist

1. Use the same journal for your marble jar metaphor to record how other people made you feel after sharing your experience. If these people are in your original list, remove or add symbols next to their names, depending on how they made you feel.

2. In your gratitude journal, thank the people who empathized with you sincerely and thank yourself for each time you empathized with another person.

3. You may use your regular meeting schedule or set aside some time for your talk on shame and empathy. It doesn't even have to be planned. Talk about it every opportunity you have.

Section Five: Curiosity and Grounded

Summary

Grounded confidence is needed, but it's also something that most of us need to discover and develop. When your childhood prompted you to armor up to protect yourself physically and emotionally, it becomes harder to rumble with vulnerability, making you lose confidence in yourself.

Similar to the concept of any sport, it's important to learn the basics of grounded confidence. In learning so, we must be patient with ourselves. It's a process of learning and unlearning. As one of Brené's interviewees said about sports, it's important to be confident in your mastery of skills to tune your focus to other matters. Leadership is the same; you must be confident in your skills to succeed.

In sports, you need to practice well enough so that by the time you are required to play under pressure, it will seem like muscle memory. Brené narrated her personal regarding the game of pool. She always thought that pool was easy. Back in her college years, she used to play while drinking.

Chaz, one of her colleagues, played pool competitively. He banished Brené's thought that her partying got in the way of her mastering this sport. Chaz explained that Brené could not excel in the game of pool because she did not play it often enough to gain muscle memory.

On the other hand, expert players make it look easy because they have practiced it more than a thousand times. Pro-players of pool modify their hits based on three elements: spin, speed, and angle. The most basic skill in pool is consistently hitting the cue stick to the cue ball. Once this fundamental skill is mastered, the rest will follow.

Brené also narrated a story from Lauren, another one of her colleagues. Lauren used to play professional soccer in Scotland. The vital skill that every soccer player must master is ball control. When Laura was a child, her coaches would ask them to do drills that focused on hitting the soccer ball using the various parts of the foot. This discipline was carried on by Laura even as she got older.

Laura shared that they had a four-foot brick wall in her house back in Scotland. She would pick a random brick and hit it a few times. Then pick another one and do the same. She said she used to do these for hours every day. Her goal? Master the art of ball control. So that when she's out on the field, she no longer worries about this skill and can focus on the gameplay and her opponents.

The sports analogy is fitting for leadership roles. During difficult conversations, leaders should have the grounded confidence to remain true to their values, learn to respond and not react, and operate with a sense of self-awareness rather than self-protection. The rumble skills allow us to show genuine concern for others, stay curious, and accept different challenges.

Brené had the opportunity to talk with the CEO, chairman, and founder of Nutanix, Dheeraj Pandey. Dheeraj emphasized the significance of vulnerability in leadership and that its absence would cause leaders to become unsuccessful in controlling the pressure of the essential paradoxes in entrepreneurship.

Here are some examples of these paradoxes:

- Paranoia and optimism
- Fierce resolve and humility
- Choice and simplicity
- Acting local and thinking global
- The quality and pace when in the process of creating new things

Dheeraj also said that leaders should equip themselves with the skills needed to endure these different tensions and be proficient at maintaining balance in life. The real measure of daring leadership is based on the ability of the leader to sustain and blossom amid opposites and paradoxes.

As leaders, it's important to consider that employees are well-provided with appropriate and informative learning materials. However, the rave about employees nowadays circles around the "easy" way of learning, usually through mobile phones. This type of learning is entertaining; however, it will not help develop strong skills.

Curiosity also plays a big role in daring leadership. Allowing yourself to be curious means that you are also allowing yourself to be vulnerable and uncertain. However, when you do, it also helps you retain information and learn better. This vulnerability is ultimately the reason why curiosity leads to grounded confidence in rumbling.

In times of discussion, our ego would respond to an issue first before learning more about the problem, but curiosity would wait and listen before giving a better solution. As Brené said in the previous chapters, when caught in a disagreement with your team, take time to discuss how you got there. Then, give your team time off and circle back to it in a few hours or the next day when everyone has already formed ideas and better solutions.

To further illustrate the connection between grounded confidence and rumbling skills, Brené shares two more stories. First from Stefan Larsson, who has turned the company Old Navy around. He started by going back to the original vision statement, and he intended to deliver that goal. In the process, he had to change the organizational structure completely. He first built a system of mutual trust, so each individual felt comfortable about sharing their insights.

Larsson made no room for judgment or blaming during their endless meetings. Outcomes were just facts, no right or wrong. They used these data to improve the overall management. Eventually, everyone became comfortable opening up. The trust that was built allowed his team to be vulnerably honest. In the process, the leaders have learned greatness through group learning.

The next story is from Dr. Sanée Bell. Dr. Bell has experience teaching students, coaching, and being a principal. Dr. Bell claimed that she was successful in leading during her first year. However, after reading more about daring leadership, she realized she still had a long way to go. The journey taught her how to practice vulnerability, increase self-awareness, and learn tools to have tough conversations.

People are not interested in how much you know if you do not show concern. Dr. Bell learned that telling her real stories made her people closer to her. She also became attuned to herself, and as an extension, she became responsive to her people's needs. Most importantly, she became brave in changing traditional methods that no longer work. She built mutual trust in her community and improved the school.

Lessons

1. It's important to be confident in rumbling skills.

2. Learning is not supposed to be easy.

3. Curiosity allows you to be completely courageous and vulnerable.

4. To get the right solution, you should analyze the problem more to understand all the aspects.

5. It does not matter how knowledgeable you are if you fail to show how much you care.

6. The lack of connection and self-awareness limits one's insights and perspective.

Issues Surrounding the Subject Matter

1. What do you think is the great barrier to being curious?

2. Why is it more difficult to unlearn rather than learn something new?

3. Why do some people find it easier to display what they know rather than show they care?

Goals

1. What must you do to develop grounded confidence?

2. Aim to learn something new each day. It does not have to be in rocket science proportion, but it could be about anything as mundane as preparing a sandwich.

3. How do you continuously encourage your team to learn within and outside their roles?

Action Steps

1. Create your self-development plan.

   a. Evaluate your rumbling skills so far.

   b. Note what skills you want to improve on and what skills you want to learn.

   c. Identify learning resources—a book, a website, or a person knowledgeable about that skill.

   d. Set a timetable for learning each skill.

2. Think of tasks you delegate to a family member, a friend, a colleague, or a team member because you lack the skills to do them, e.g., using the coffee machine. Choose one to learn each day.

3. Research training resources for your team that is not considered easy but rather appropriate.

4. Work with your team members on their individual development plans.

5. You may also share the following stories to start a discussion. You may also use them to inspire your team and learn from them.

   a. Stefan Larsson's story on how he completely brought back an almost-failing company to its feet

   b. Dr. Sanée Bell's story of how she continuously improved her leadership and applied her learning from the author

Checklist

1. Create a development plan template, so you and your team members have the same format.

2. Prepare a list of things you want or need to learn. Cross out an item as you learn it.

3. Agree with each team member on how you can monitor their learning progress.

Part Two: Living Into Our Values

Summary

When we agree to go to the arena, it's usually because of our values - principles we believe are important in our life. If we fail to be clear on our values, the critics and cynics around us will succeed in bringing us down. Our values are very important because when everything is going hard, it will become the sole reason that reminds us why we started in the first place.

Living into our values means we practice them in our daily lives. It's more than simply stating them; it's putting them at the center of our actions. Brené shared three steps on how to start doing so.

The first is to identify the certain set of values we live for. You can search the list of the values that exist. It's tempting to choose many, but you should be able to nail down two core values. Trimming your list down is important because having too many values means they're unimportant.

Second-tier values also exist. These are the values that branch down from your core values. Brené shared that when she chose hers, faith and courage, she wanted to choose family too. But when she analyzed it, her love for her family stemmed from her core values, not an addition to them. There's a downloadable PDF File of the list of values on Brené's website. You may use it as a reference in choosing yours, but it would be better if you could identify your values without the influence of a reference.

The second step is identifying at least three to four behaviors (or actions) that support our chosen values and another set that counters them. For Brené, one courageous behavior she has is to speak up when needed, especially when fighting for what is right. At the same time, one of her faith behaviors is not engaging and speaking the dehumanizing language, even when she is right.

Identifying these behaviors to test how much we live by our core values is important. It's also important to point out actions or experiences where we went against them. It's tough work to call yourself out but holding yourself accountable, and unlearning wrongdoings are both parts of self-development.

In this process of learning to live into our values, many negative spectators will doubt and judge as an attempt to silence you. Imagine being in an arena and noticing these haters; it will be hard. But then, in these arena seats, you also have your biggest supporters - your self-compassion and empathy team. The third and final step is to identify who these people are.

Your empathy team includes the people who will support you in living your values despite it being a challenge for themselves. They should also be the same people who will call you out if you did something outside of your values and would let you know why, while your self-compassion is how you treat yourself. For Brené, it mostly revolves in taking care of herself well and putting her health first over her work.

As established, we all have different sets of values. But regardless of what we pick, the brave leaders don't stay quiet about the difficult topics. Brené, for example, recognizes her privilege. She's white, straight, and educated. Granted, she does have a lot to fight for her gender, but it does not make her less privileged.

She shares that almost all the companies she visited struggle to discuss race. Her default suggestion is to first listen to the talk about race. It's a fact that they will make mistakes along the way, which will be greatly uncomfortable. But no matter how difficult the journey is, a daring leader should never be silent. Choosing not to discuss this is the embodiment of privilege.

Silence is not welcome in a daring leadership and is not an element of courageous cultures. These hard conversations cannot be predetermined, which means to say you can't prepare answers for these issues, but it's okay. A daring leader does not need to have all the answers, nor do they ease perfect discussions on difficult topics. Rather it's someone who acknowledges the problem, listens to it, and continues to ask questions about it.

A brave leader is empathetic, and we all can promote empathy. During challenging conversations on race, gender equality, etc., a brave leader must fight against judgment, secrecy, and silence. It's the only way to eliminate shame in the workplace, so it's important to have a strong empathy section behind you.

On the other hand, self-compassion is easy to talk about but very difficult to live by. For Brené, it's healthy food, sleep, connection, and exercise. When she lives by these elements in her life, it's an indicator that she is living into her values. She must be in good shape spiritually, physically, and emotionally. Meanwhile, resentment indicates when she is not living up to her values.

Brené used to ask herself what it feels like when she's living into her values. For years, she thought it would be easy to determine this and that the easy option would be the right choice. But contrary to what she first thought, Brené realized that her values present themselves when she must choose between two difficult decisions. She no longer looks for beautiful moments but for quiet times when she feels strong.

One of the biggest challenges we face when trying to live with our values is receiving and giving feedback. The key is to know when you are ready to do so. Some key signs show when you are ready to give someone feedback. Below is a guideline.

1. <u>When you are ready to sit next to the person you are giving the feedback to, not across from them.</u>

A massive desk between two people isn't just about placement in a corporate set-up. When something important needs to be discussed, a table creates more space between two people who need to be connected. Sometimes, it also portrays the differential of power.

2. <u>When you are willing to place the issue in front of both of you and not just between you</u>

It's as easy as changing the dialogue from saying "You're wrong" to "This needs to be changed." When you sit side by side and view the issue from the same perspective, you can focus on resolving the issue rather than point at each other's errors.

3. <u>When you are genuinely ready to listen, ask essential questions, and accept that you may not completely comprehend the issue.</u>

During feedback sessions, we must remember that we are listening to give feedback and not to teach a lesson. When someone is opening up to you, narrate to them how you understood the situation and ask for clarification. Do not be afraid to have multiple sessions and "circle back" the next day.

4. <u>When you are ready to recognize what the other person is good at rather than focusing on their wrongdoings</u>

This indicator is difficult to show when working on a tight deadline. But simply pointing out mistakes and pressuring them to correct them won't help your side either. It's demotivating to be scolded, making it difficult for the person to deliver well. Instead, take the time to appreciate before offering help to resolve the missing parts.

5. <u>When you acknowledge the other person's strengths and use them to conquer challenges</u>

Each team member of your company has a different skill set. Observe if this member is utilizing their strength to work on a project in resolving issues. If not, highlight this strength and tell them how they can use it to improve the overall task and, ultimately, the company. If you are too angry to notice these strengths, it's not a good time to give feedback.

6. <u>When you're ready to hold them accountable without blaming or shaming</u>

Sadly, most of us were raised in a household wherein feedback was shown through blaming or shaming. This situation is why many of us struggle to provide productive feedback and constructive criticism. You must only provide feedback once you are confident enough that you trust yourself not to do the same.

7. <u>When you are ready to acknowledge your mistake</u>

The previous section, The Call to Courage, discussed that giving feedback requires the person to own up to their part. If you admit that you are wrong, the person you are talking to will be more confident in opening up and explaining their side.

8. <u>When you can genuinely appreciate someone's effort and not criticize them</u>

Appreciation goes a long way. Remember that your team members are also humans. It's normal to make mistakes, and it's your job to give them the needed suggestions to improve them. However, it's also your role to ensure they get the acknowledgment needed for the effort they have contributed.

9. <u>When you can openly talk about resolutions that would lead to opportunity and growth</u>

It's easy to point out wrongs; however, the challenge is explaining their part in the big picture. You must make the person understand how vital their role is in the overall growth and opportunity of the business and to the person himself.

10. <u>When you can portray the same openness and vulnerability, you expect from the other person.</u>

When we give feedback to another person, we expect them to accept whatever we say wholeheartedly. Likewise, we must display the similar behavior and emotion we expect from them. We need to mirror our expectations with what we are showing.

Remember to bring your values when giving feedback. How do you want the receiving end to perceive you and your words? Values should come into play. It's also important when receiving feedback. Regardless of who the person may be, you should be able to react in a way aligned with your core values.

It's also important to note that we can never fully know a person unless we know and understand their values. Brené shared a few stories about how shocked her team's values were when they had already known each other for so long. It also helped develop their relationship within and outside work.

Organizations have their core values as well. For Brené's company, it's courage, stewardship, and how they care for each other and themselves. As a leader, you must ensure that these values are transformed into operationalized values. This intended transformation means there should be actionable items that can be done in practicing said values.

Operationalized values improve decision-making because it's easy to be decisive and thoughtful when the values guide the process. Some companies have plastered their values all over the establishment with big, colorful posters but rarely call out people who go against them. Organizations that try to actualize these core values have a smoother flow in management.

Lessons

1. It's important to be clear on what your values are to be able to live by them.

2. A person should not have too many values because it's unrealistic and would lose meaning.

3. You must know a person's core values before fully knowing them.

4. Values are the weapons we need when we go out and fight in the arena of life. We use it to protect what's important to us.

5. We have to set our values first before trying to live into them.

6. It's not true that we can separate work and personal values; we only have one set, which applies to every aspect of our lives.

Issues surrounding the subject matter

1. What values do you think define you completely?

2. What values do you have that are not aligned with your company values? How so? What do you intend to do about it?

3. Why do you think it's difficult to be consistent in living by core values? What's the biggest struggle? How do you plan on overcoming it?

4. Identify situations where you're being tested on your values. Did you act by them or not? Take time to analyze how you reacted.

5. Who are the people who belong on your empathy team? Why are they there? Do they deserve to be on that

team? Why or why not? Think of situations that made them deserve a place on your team. Were there situations when you doubted their place in your team? What was the situation, and how did it make you

Goals

1. Set your core values.

2. Learn how to start living by this set of principles.

3. Train your team members on how to set their core values.

Action Steps

1. Identify your core values (maximum: two) and write them somewhere you can always see them. Name key behaviors that support these values.

2. Conduct a values-sharing exercise with your team. Just like the three steps illustrated, let them identify their core values and identify behaviors that support and counter them.

3. Encourage your team members also to choose their empathy team. Discuss its importance in practicing values.

Checklist

1. Start with questions like:

   a. What do I value the most in life?

   b. What is that one thing I will never give up, no matter the cost?

   c. What legacy do I want to leave behind? What non-material thing do I want to be remembered for?

2. Create a unique banner that documents your values and the supporting behavior to serve as a constant reminder. Have your team do the same.

Part Three: Braving Trust

Summary

Most of us view ourselves as trustworthy, so when someone says we are not or someone refuses to trust us, we tend to be defensive about it. Charles Feltman's book describes trust as choosing to risk something of value to become vulnerable to another's actions, while mistrust is deciding something valuable is not safe with a certain person.

Since trust is a heavy topic, people tend to shy away from talking about it, so, in defense, we talk about the person instead. It's difficult since trust holds a group together, and without it, trust issues could affect performance and overall organizational success.

To talk about trust is crucial. Some leaders only open up to trust issues when something irreversible has already happened, leaving the concerned person demoralized as it's the first time they hear about the trust issues. It needs to be discussed as soon as possible to allow the people and organization to improve.

Brené made the acronym **BRAVING** to list down the behaviors that define trust:

- **B**oundaries – It's about respecting each other's boundaries, and if they are not clear, questions for clarification should be asked.
- **R**eliability – This behavior refers to a person's ability to deliver what is promised without delay.
- **A**ccountability – It's about owning up to mistakes, apologizing, and doing something to make up for what was wrongly done.
- **V**ault – Others' secrets or confessions are not yours to share. This behavior refers to keeping other people's vulnerable moments to yourself.
- **I**ntegrity – It's doing what's right, even if it's not the easy choice.
- **N**onjudgment – This behavior refers to a person's freedom to share with and ask you for something without judgment.
- **G**enerosity – This behavior extends the most giving expression through actions, words, and intentions.

Brené designed the **BRAVING** inventory to assess the trust among the different team members. She also shared a story from one of the leaders who used this inventory with his team. The scenario is an example of how Reliability is played out. During a meeting facilitated by this leader, his teammate opened up about the leader not being punctual during their meetings due to unexpected schedule shifts.

The teammate said that he felt like the leader did not fully value their time because of the last-minute delays and cancellations. To resolve this, they agreed that the leader should set meetings with enough allowance so they will not be affected during scheduled shifts. The leader was honest that if they did not do the inventory, he would not know it was becoming an issue.

Similar to the term used with emotions, we also unpack each one of the BRAVING inventory to analyze the problem. An example is when Brené was refused promotion by Javier, which he said was because of confidentiality issues. Brené was surprised and said she never shared anything discussed within their office. Javier agreed; however, he also pointed out that Brené shared stories with him that was not hers to share.

As they unpacked Vault, Brené realized that this side of confidentiality is often neglected. We claim to a certain person that we have never shared their secret with others. But ironically, we shared others' secrets with them. If it happened between you and another person, technically, the confidence between you was not broken, but the other person also witnessed how careless you were in sharing others'.

Another one is integrity. It's usual for people to go the easy way even though it's not the right way. It's also tempting because almost everyone prefers to do it this way, and even some of them succeed. Still, it doesn't make it right. Brené suggested having an integrity partner who keeps us in check whether we are doing right by our integrity or not.

From the BRAVING Inventory, nonjudgment is one of the toughest elements. We desire to judge others. This desire is common in situations that we find personally challenging. We pick someone who does worse than us and thinks we are better off than the other person. It then leads to refusing help or judging someone else who asks for help. When in a place of nonjudgment, everyone simply encourages help.

Brené gives an example of generosity by sharing a story by Dara Schmidt, the director of Cedar Rapids Library. Remember that generosity is setting up clear boundaries. Why? It's because it allows the person to become generous with their actions, words, and intentions.

Dara used to think that people made her crazy, especially when nobody was listening to her. But then, when she came across Brené's Daring Leadership teachings, she realized that her own expectations and assumptions made her go crazy. It became her major red flag. With this knowledge, she changed her leadership style. She made sure to provide clear expectations and boundaries. She was satisfied with her team's performance after this change.

Trust is something that needs to be earned over time. There are several moments piled up that make a person trustworthy. It's not something you can demand spot-on. Sometimes, people say, "You need to trust me," to others in crisis. Sadly, it doesn't work that way, and you will only find yourself deeper in the crisis. So to be trustworthy, you must continue to show that you are before you get there.

The foundation of trust stems from our ability to trust ourselves. Often due to failures and disappointments, we tend to lose trust in ourselves. At this point, it's best to do an unpacking. Go back to when something caused you to lose trust and review each element of the BRAVING Inventory. It will help you pinpoint the exact issue that needs to be focused on.

Remember that you are in control in your relationship with the trust, which means you are also accountable for where you are lacking. Remember that trust is founded on a pile of small moments in your improvement journey. You must commit to building these moments for yourself to make up for what you are missing. We can't give something we don't have, so what can we offer if we don't trust ourselves?

Lessons

1. Seeing ourselves as trustworthy and being perceived by others as trustworthy are two different things.

2. Trust holds together families, organizations, friendships, and all types of relationships.

3. Trust needs to be regularly talked about to achieve success in companies.

4. Self-trust is important so others can learn how to trust us.

Issues surrounding the subject matter

1. Do you think others see you as trustworthy? How so?

2. Why is trust a difficult topic to discuss? Why does it make people uncomfortable?

3. Do you truly trust yourself? If not, why do you think so? How do you plan on resolving it?

Goals

1. Preach and practice trust within yourself and toward your community.

2. Keep communication open in discussing trust.

3. Learn how to resolve trust issues without being defensive.

Action Steps

1. Identify your level of self-trust by doing a BRAVING inventory.

2. Ask your team to do their respective BRAVING inventory.

3. Hold a trust session to discuss the answers in the BRAVING Inventory and provide solutions to issues.

4. Agree with your team on when to review the BRAVING inventory to keep track of changes.

Checklist

1. Print the BRAVING Inventory worksheet available on Brené's website and distribute it to your team members.

2. Calendar your BRAVING inventory progress review.

3. Recognize efforts made by each team member to change for the better.

Part Four: Learning To Rise

Based on research, leaders who were taught risking skills are most likely to engage in risky situations because they're confident that they know how to rise back up. Similar to skydiving, you first learn how to land before you fly. Learning rising skills after an event of failure isn't motivating or effective.

Brené stated an example in a school context. Parents nowadays usually go out of their way to pave the way for their children rather than preparing them for the difficult path ahead. Additionally, Brené stated how millennials in her company were moved by how it became easy for them to talk about uncomfortable topics.

When being brave and daring, failure is a guarantee. But if you are not equipped with the necessary tools to get back up, you will not even risk it. This part includes the rising process, which is composed of the following: the reckoning, the rumble, and the revolution.

In the reckoning, you recognize that you are hooked emotionally and curious about it. When in this process, we tend to power over other people as a defensive act. We also bounce hurt in a way that we deny ever being hurt because it's easier than to talk about it. Others would numb it off or stockpile all the hurtful situations. While others act as if everything is just awesome and positive, rather than admitting something's wrong.

There's an effective strategy of breathing where you hold it first before exhaling. This strategy calms down the emotion we're feeling inside. It allows us to get a hold of our reaction before overreacting.

In rumbling, this is where we tend to create stories in our minds when we lack the needed data to understand the actual situation. Fear fills in the data gaps, which means our fear causes us to create unnecessary issues that aren't even there due to anxiety and stress.

To counter this, we must ask the right questions first. Because if we simply just ask, we could get the wrong answers. First, make it clear that what you are assuming is happening. Then, clarify what additional data you need to know. Lastly, analyze yourself and your feeling.

Finally, we have reached the revolution. As said in Brené's words, "Courage is rebellion." We must learn how to speak against the uncomfortable wrongdoings of what's happening in our world. To be vulnerably honest is an act of ultimate resistance, even in just words. You will be pissing off lots of people on this journey, but it will be worth it.

This journey of daring leadership will not be an easy ride. By now, it's obvious that one needs to be able to be brave enough to succeed. In Brené's parting message, choose courage over comfort and whole hearts over armor.

Lessons

1. Before risking being courageous, you must first learn how to rise after failure.

2. There's a way to resolve failures without bursting or lashing out.

3. Revolution is scary, but it's the way to improve the world by speaking up when it's easier to be silent.

Issues surrounding the subject matter

1. Have you caused a crisis, knowingly or unknowingly? How did it feel to know you caused it? What are your emotional cues?

2. Based on the three-part process, what's the most difficult part in rising back up again? What makes it difficult?

3. What are the challenges that prevent you from daring to lead?

Goals

1. Learn how to maximize calmness when in the middle of an issue.

2. Learn how to rise to have the courage to fall.

3. Be able to walk the talk of becoming courageous and daring.

Action Steps

1. Identify some emotional cues that commonly portray themselves when you're in a crisis. Map out steps to control them.

2. Create a joy and meaning list and make it a guideline on how you see success for yourself.

3. Conduct the story rumble within your group.

Checklist

1. Use courage-building skills, practices, and tools. The step-by-step process is seen on Brené's website.

2. Beyond that, you can brainstorm about what courage building skills and tools which you can develop to further aid you in your journey.

Epilogue

Dare to Lead aims to teach leadership honestly and cruelly, focusing on discussing all the difficult and uncomfortable topics that need to be covered in a successful leader. With Brené Brown's stories of personal experience and case studies from interviewees, the reader will understand the importance of each part and section.

By the end of the book, the reader will be able to have a realization that daring leadership isn't something that can be learned easily or just by reading this book. It includes continuous practice and endless rumbles with teammates. It's the act of constant improvement, development, and learning.

Brené shared that in her research for this book, she learned three important things:

- The organization's collective courage is the best indicator of the organization's chance to be successful in practicing its culture, meeting its mission, and developing its leaders.
- Building courage is the most difficult challenge in developing leaders. But it can be learned through utilizing the tools and skills learned in rumbling with vulnerability, living into core values, braving with trust, and learning how to rise.
- The early onset of failure is letting someone else's definition of success affect ours. We are the only ones who can define our success because it should reflect who we are and what we are truly fighting for.

Dare to Lead promises to develop daring and brave leaders. It surely does that.

Made in the USA
Monee, IL
08 June 2023

f87df61d-dcb0-483b-8a83-437835e55300R01